# Play Easy Recorder

Published by:
**Chester Music Limited**
8/9 Frith Street, London W1D 3JB, England.

Exclusive distributors:
**Music Sales Limited**
Distribution Centre, Newmarket Road,
Bury St Edmunds, Suffolk IP33 3YB.

**Music Sales Pty Limited**
120 Rothschild Avenue, Rosebery,
NSW 2018, Australia.

Order No. CH66935
ISBN 1-84449-079-3
This book © Copyright 2003 by Chester Music.

Compiled and edited by Heather Ramage.
All arrangements by Jerry Lanning
unless stated otherwise.
Music engraved by Jerry Lanning.

Printed in the United Kingdom by
Caligraving Limited, Thetford, Norfolk.

www.musicsales.com

**Chester Music Limited**
London / New York / Paris / Sydney /
Copenhagen / Berlin / Madrid / Tokyo

## Christmas

# Angels From The Realms Of Glory

Words by James Montgomery
Music Traditional

An-gels from the_ realms of glo-ry, wing your_flight o'er_ all the earth;

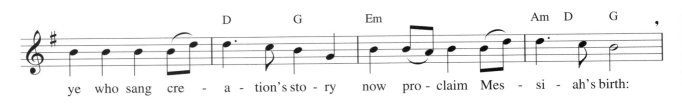

ye who sang cre - a - tion's sto - ry now pro - claim Mes - si - ah's birth:

Come_____ and_ wor - ship

Christ the new - born King,_____ come_____

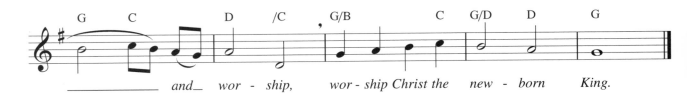

_____ and_ wor - ship, wor - ship Christ the new - born King.

# Away In A Manger

Words Traditional
Music by William Kirkpatrick

# Coventry Carol

Traditional

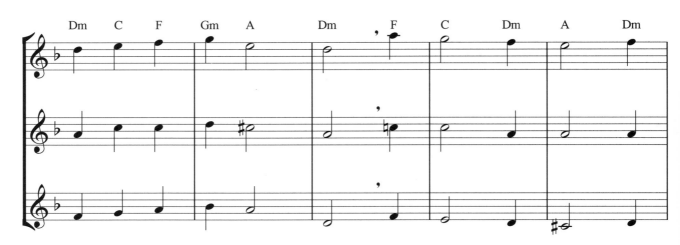

*Lully, lulla, thou little tiny child,*
*By by, lully lullay.*
O sisters too, how may we do
For to preserve this day
This poor youngling, for whom we do sing,
By by, lully lullay?

# I Saw Three Ships

## Traditional

**Gently moving** ♩. = 68

I saw three ships come sail-ing in, *on Christ-mas Day, on Christ-mas Day,* I

saw three ships come sail-ing in, *on Christ-mas day in the morn-ing.*

# Deck The Hall

**Traditional**

**Brightly** ♩ = 132

Deck the hall with boughs of hol-ly, fa la la la la la la la la,

'Tis the sea-son to be jol-ly, fa la la la la la la la la.

Fill the mead cup, drain the bar-rel, fa la la la la la la la la,

Troll the an-cient Christ-mas car-ol, fa la la la la la la la la.

# Ding Dong! Merrily On High

**Words by George Woodward**
**Music Traditional**

**Lively** ♩ = 132

Ding dong! Mer-ri-ly on high in heav'n the bells are ring-ing.

Ding dong! Ver-i-ly the sky is riv'n with an-gels sing-ing.

# It Came Upon The Midnight Clear

Words by Edmund Hamilton Sears
Music Traditional

# Happy Xmas (War Is Over)

### Words & Music by John Lennon & Yoko Ono

**With a lilt** ♩. = 56

*mf* So this is Christ-mas and what have you done? An-oth-er year

ov-er, a new one just be - gun;___ And so this is Christ-mas,

I hope you have fun, the near and the dear ones, the old and the

young.___ A mer-ry, mer-ry Christ-mas___ and a hap-py New Year,

let's hope it's a good one___ with-out an-y fear. And so this is

Christ-mas for weak and for strong, the rich and the poor ones,

the road is so___ long. And so, hap-py Christ-mas, for black and for

white, for the yel - low and red ones let's stop all the fights.

A mer - ry, mer - ry Christ - mas and a hap - py New Year,

let's hope it's a good one with - out an - y fear.

# O Christmas Tree (O Tannenbaum)

Traditional

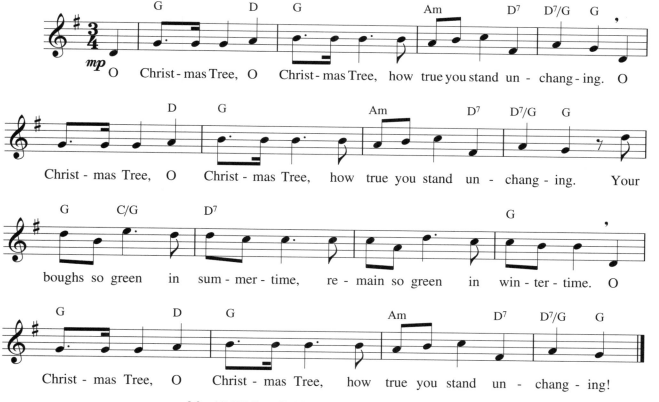

O Christ - mas Tree, O Christ - mas Tree, how true you stand un - chang - ing. O

Christ - mas Tree, O Christ - mas Tree, how true you stand un - chang - ing. Your

boughs so green in sum - mer - time, re - main so green in win - ter - time. O

Christ - mas Tree, O Christ - mas Tree, how true you stand un - chang - ing!

# Hark! The Herald Angels Sing

Words by Charles Wesley
Music by Felix Mendelssohn

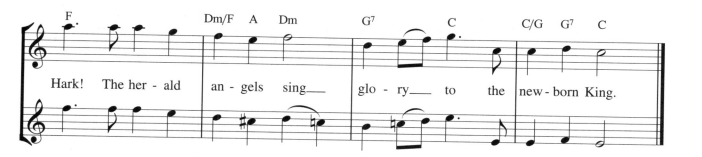

# I Believe In Father Christmas

Words & Music by Greg Lake & Peter Sinfield

# I Saw Mommy Kissing Santa Claus

Words & Music by Tommie Connor

# Joy To The World

Words by Isaac Watts
Music by George Frideric Handel

# Jingle Bells

Words & Music by J.S. Pierpont
Arranged by Heather Ramage

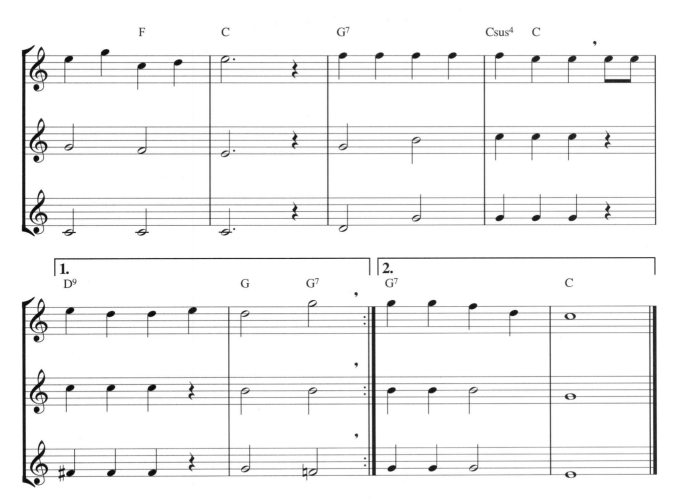

We're dashing through the snow,
In a one-horse open sleigh,
Across the fields we go;
We're laughing all the way.

The bells on bobtails ring,
They are making spirits bright,
What fun it is to ride and sing
A sleighing song tonight.

Chorus x 2
*Oh, jingle bells, jingle bells,*
*Jingle all the way.*
*Oh what fun it is to ride*
*In a one-horse open sleigh!*

# Jingle Bell Rock

### Words & Music by Joseph Beal & James Boothe

clock. Mix and min - gle in a jin - gl - in' beat, that's the jin - gle bell rock.

# In Dulci Jubilo

Traditional
English Words by R.L. Pearsall

In dul - ci ju - bi - lo_____ let us our

hom - age show;_____ Our heart's joy re - cli - neth

in prae - se - pi - o,_____ and like a bright star shin -

neth ma - tris in gre - mi - o;_____ Al - pha

es et O!_____ Al - pha es et O!_____

# Mary's Boy Child

Words & Music by Jester Hairston

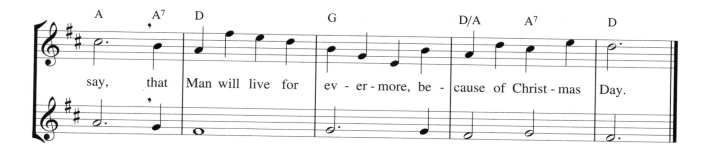

# O Come, All Ye Faithful

Original Words & Music by John Francis Wade
English Words by Frederick Oakeley

# Once In Royal David's City

Words by Cecil Alexander
Music by Henry Gauntlett

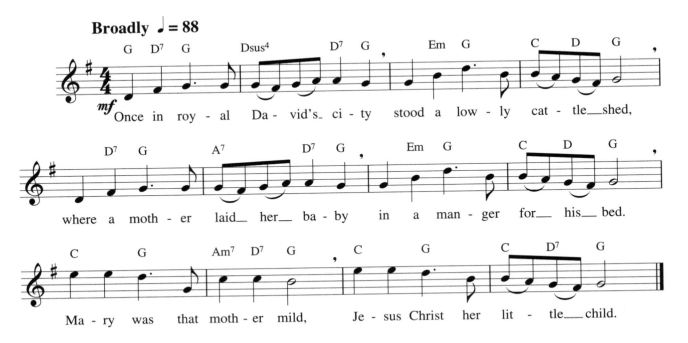

Once in roy - al Da - vid's ci - ty stood a low - ly cat - tle shed,
where a moth - er laid her ba - by in a man - ger for his bed.
Ma - ry was that moth - er mild, Je - sus Christ her lit - tle child.

# O Little Town Of Bethlehem

Words by Phillips Brooks
Music by Lewis Redner

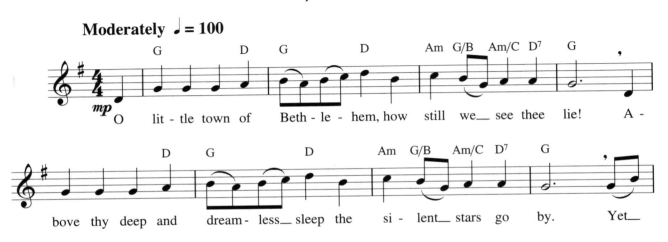

O lit - tle town of Beth - le - hem, how still we see thee lie! A -
bove thy deep and dream - less sleep the si - lent stars go by. Yet

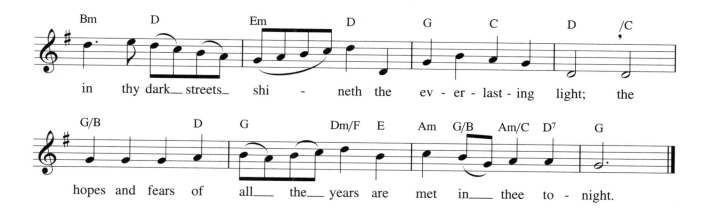

in thy dark streets shi - neth the ev - er - last - ing light; the

hopes and fears of all the years are met in thee to - night.

# O Come, O Come, Emmanuel

Traditional
English Words by John Neale

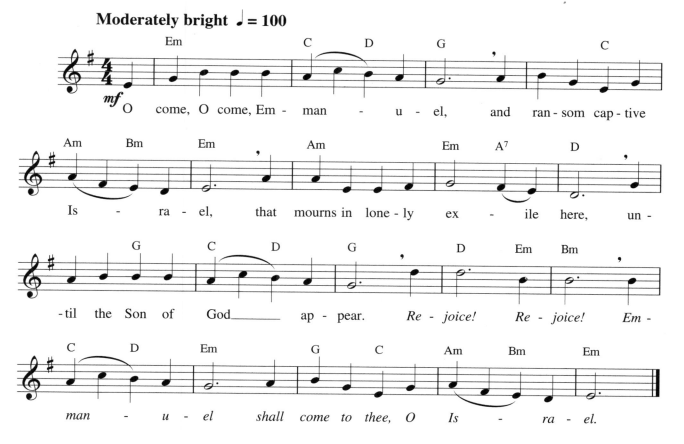

Moderately bright ♩ = 100

O come, O come, Em - man - u - el, and ran - som cap - tive

Is - ra - el, that mourns in lone - ly ex - ile here, un -

-til the Son of God ap - pear. Re - joice! Re - joice! Em -

man - u - el shall come to thee, O Is - ra - el.

# O Holy Night

By A. Adam

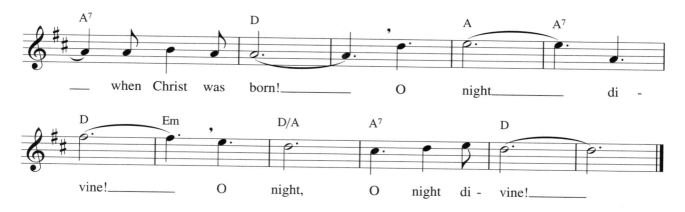

when Christ was born! O night di -
vine! O night, O night di - vine!

# Past Three O'Clock

Words Traditional
Music by George Woodward

Past three o' - clock, on a cold fros - ty morn - ing,

past three o' - clock; good mor - row mas - ters all! Born is a

ba - by, gen - tle as may be, Son of the e - ter - nal

Fath - er su - per - nal. Past three o' - clock, on a cold fros - ty

morn - ing, past three o' - clock; good mor - row mas - ters all!

# Silent Night

Words by Joseph Mohr
Music by Franz Grüber

# The First Noël

Traditional

Moderately ♩ = 80

The\_ first\_ No - ël, the\_ an - gel did say, was to

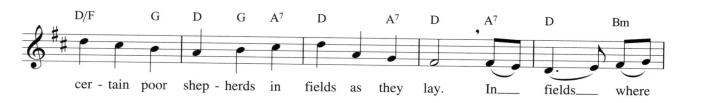

cer - tain poor shep - herds in fields as they lay. In\_ fields\_ where

they lay\_ keep - ing their sheep, on a cold win - ter's night\_ that

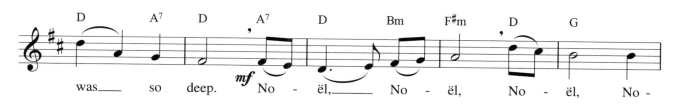

was\_ so deep. No - ël,\_ No - ël, No - ël, No -

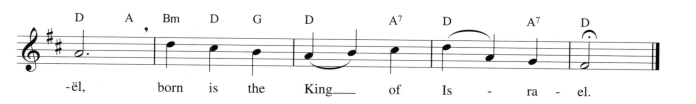

-ël, born is the King\_ of Is - ra - el.

# See Amid The Winter's Snow

Words by Edward Caswall
Music by John Goss

See a-mid the win-ter's snow, born for us on earth be-low,
see the ten-der Lamb ap-pears, pro-mised from e-ter-nal years.
Hail, thou ev-er bless-ed morn, hail, re-demp-tion's hap-py dawn!
Sing through all Je-ru-sa-lem, Christ is born in Beth-le-hem.

# The Holly And The Ivy

Traditional

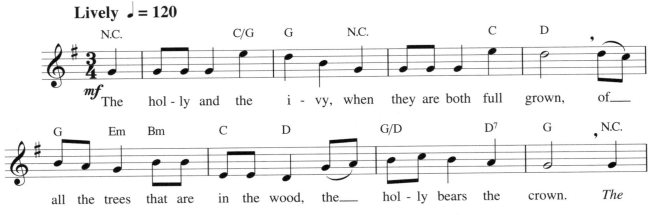

The hol-ly and the i-vy, when they are both full grown, of____
all the trees that are in the wood, the____ hol-ly bears the crown. The

ris - ing of the sun____ and the run - ning of the deer, the____

play - ing of the mer - ry or - gan, sweet sing - ing in the choir.

# We Three Kings Of Orient Are

Words & Music by John Henry Hopkins

**Gently moving** ♩. = 48

We three kings of O - ri - ent are; bear - ing gifts we tra - verse a - far.

Field and foun - tain, moor and moun - tain, fol - low - ing yon - der star. O____

star of won - der, star of night, star with roy - al beau - ty bright,

west - ward lead - ing, still pro - ceed - ing, guide us to thy per - fect light.

# Winter Wonderland

Words by Richard Smith
Music by Felix Bernard
Arranged by Heather Ramage

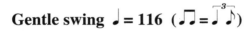

I: Sleigh bells ring, are you list-'ning? In the lane snow is

glist-'ning, a, beau-ti-ful sight,__ we're hap-py to-night,__

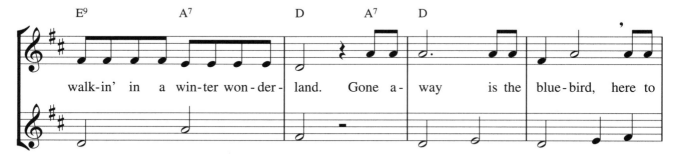

walk-in' in a win-ter won-der-land. Gone a-way is the blue-bird, here to

stay is a new bird, he sings a love-song_ as we go a-long,__

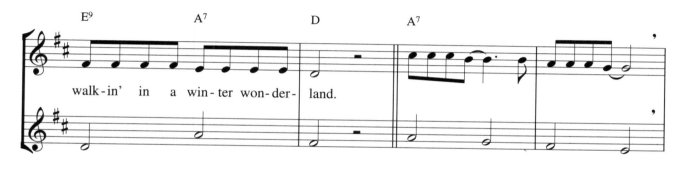

walk-in' in a win-ter won-der-land.

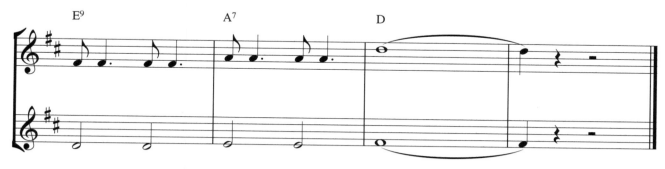

# While Shepherds Watched

Words by Nahum Tate
Music Traditional

While shep-herds watched their flocks by night, all seat-ed on the ground, the an-gel of the Lord came down, and glo-ry shone a-round.

# Home For The Holidays

Words & Music by Al Stillman & Robert Allen
Arranged by Heather Ramage

Oh, there's no place like home for the holidays,
'Cause no matter how far away you roam,
When you pine for the sunshine of a friendly gaze,
For the holidays you can't beat home sweet home.

I met a man who lives in Tennessee
And he was heading for Pennsylvania,
And some homemade pumpkin pie.
From Pennsylvania folks are trav'lin' down
To Dixie's sunny shore,
From Atlantic to Pacific, gee, the traffic is terrific.

# Frosty The Snowman

### Words & Music by Steve Nelson & Jack Rollins